Shell-Flower

by Rhonda Rodriguez
illustrated by Craig Spearing

HOUGHTON MIFFLIN BOSTON

They came with guns that made lightning and sounded like thunder. They came with hair on their white faces. The white men arrived in Paiute (PIE-yoot) country, and they came like great roaring lions.

Shell-Flower was still a very little girl when the news arrived for the first time: White men were nearby.

Shell-Flower's grandfather was the chief of all the Paiute people. When he heard the news, he jumped up and clapped his hands. "My white brothers!" he cried. "They have finally come!"

Grandfather had heard of the white people from far away. He called them his long-lost brothers. He wanted to meet them. Grandfather went to greet the strangers.

Grandfather took a band of men with him. He came to the white men's camp, but they would not meet with him. They turned him away.

Still, Grandfather was filled with hope. He had seen his white brothers for the first time. He returned to Shell-Flower's village and told this story.

In the beginning of the world, there were four children. There was one dark boy, one light boy, one dark girl, and one light girl.

When the children were young, they got along well. But as they grew older, they argued. This made their mother and father sad.

"Why do you argue? You are family," the father said.

The children were ashamed. But there was no peace among them. The parents could bear it no longer.

"If you cannot be good to each other, then you must remain apart," the father said. "Go across the great ocean. Stay out of each other's lives."

The dark girl and boy left together. They went to one side of the ocean. They were the first people of our nation.

The light boy and girl went to the other side of the ocean. They became the white people's nation.

We have waited all this time for someone to come to us from the white nation, to bring us together again.

Years passed. Grandfather finally met his white brothers. He traveled to their cities in California. He grew to admire and even love his white brothers. Every spring he returned to the Paiute homeland. He told Shell-Flower and her people about the wonders of the white brothers.

"They build houses that can travel," Grandfather said. "Some of their houses travel over the ocean, blown by the wind. They are faster than our horses! Other houses travel across the land on wheels."

One of the white brothers, John Fremont, had given Grandfather a paper. "When we show this to our lost brothers and sisters, it will tell them who we are," Grandfather said. "No harm will come to us when they see it."

For a time, Shell-Flower also longed to meet the white people.

Then came the awful spring when the Paiutes heard terrible news of the white man. Grandfather was away in California, and Shell-Flower's father was now Chief of the Paiutes. Shell-Flower's father was not as trusting of the white brothers. "They look like owls," he said.

Stories came from other tribes that the white brothers were killing many native people. The adults told Shell-Flower of horrible things that the white brothers were doing.

Shell-Flower was terrified. "How could Grandfather admire such men?" she wondered.

Shell-Flower's father sent his people into the mountains to hide for the winter.

One day, an alarm passed through Shell-Flower's camp: "The white people are coming!" Everyone began to run.

Shell-Flower's baby sister was strapped on Mother's back. Mother grabbed Shell-Flower's hand. They ran through the camp. Shell-Flower was so afraid, her legs could not keep up. Shell-Flower's aunt also had a small girl who could not run fast enough.

"We must hide our girls!" cried Shell-Flower's aunt.

The two mothers dug holes into the earth. They lowered each girl into a hole up to her neck. They filled the holes with soft soil. They placed sage bushes over the girls' faces to protect them from the sun. "Do not make a sound," said Shell-Flower's mother. "The earth will keep you safe."

Then Mother and Aunt ran off.

Shell-Flower and her cousin stayed quiet. They did not even whisper to each other. Fear pounded inside them. What if the white people found them?

For hours, Shell-Flower waited for something terrible to happen. Day turned to night.

Then, in the darkness, Shell-Flower heard low voices. Footsteps came close. Shell-Flower's throat closed in terror. "Here. Here they are," said a voice. It was her mother and father! The two children were lifted out of their holes. With Father's arms around her, Shell-Flower slowly stopped trembling.

Shell-Flower would never forget that terrible day. It made her fear the white brothers that Grandfather so loved.

Later that year, other white men destroyed the Paiutes' food and winter supplies. Shell-Flower's father gathered his people and told of a terrible dream he had had. In it, the land of the Paiute was overrun by the white men. Many Paiutes were killed. "To avoid bloodshed, we must all go to hide in the mountains. When my father returns, he will tell us what to do," Shell-Flower's father told his people.

But when Grandfather returned, he did not share his son's fear. He now wanted Shell-Flower and her family to come with him to California. He would bring Shell-Flower to meet his white brothers.

The journey to California began in the late fall. Grandfather led many Paiute families. Shell-Flower traveled with her mother, her brothers, and her sisters. Her father remained in the homeland with the rest of the Paiute people.

Shell-Flower rode behind one of her brothers. They traveled along a river and camped each night. On the third day, some men who had gone ahead came back to the group. "We have seen our white brothers' houses up ahead," they reported.

"Stop here," Grandfather told the group. "I will go to meet them."

Grandfather returned with gifts of food from his white brothers. "I showed them my paper. As long as I have it, we are safe," he said. "We will camp near the white brothers tonight."

Shell-Flower remembered the time she had been buried. This time, she hid under her brother's fur robe. As the horses began to move ahead, she cried against his back.

"Please, let's camp somewhere else tonight," said Shell-Flower's mother. "My daughter is too frightened."

Grandfather agreed. As the group rode by the white men's houses, Shell-Flower kept her head under the robe. She did not want to see.

But soon Shell-Flower finally saw the white strangers for the first time. Grandfather brought two white men back to meet the group of travelers. The men smiled at Shell-Flower and bent down to meet her.

"Hide me!" cried Shell-Flower. She ran behind her mother. When the men came even closer, Shell-Flower peeked out. "The owls!" she cried.

Both Grandfather and the white men laughed. The strangers were kind and gentle.

Still, that night, Shell-Flower lay awake, seeing owl eyes everywhere.

The families soon stopped outside of one of the strangers' towns. Grandfather took Shell-Flower's brothers and older sister with him. They came back with wonderful stories of red stone houses and whistling steamboats.

Shell-Flower's brothers had met the strangers. They had not been afraid. Nothing bad had happened.

"Perhaps Grandfather's words are right," Shell-Flower thought.

One day, Shell-Flower's brother brought a new food for her to try. It was from the strangers. They called it *cake*. The taste was so sweet that Shell-Flower could not stop eating it. She had never had anything quite like it.

The next day Shell-Flower was sick.

Mother looked at Shell-Flower's swollen face and touched her hot skin. She held Shell-Flower close as she spoke to Grandfather. "Your white brothers gave us food that made my daughter sick," she said.

Shell-Flower could not open her eyes. She heard her grandfather speak to her mother. "I do not think that the cake has harmed her," he said. "I have eaten it, and so have you. No one else is sick."

Shell-Flower's sickness lasted many days.

As she lay with her eyes swollen shut, she heard a soft voice. She felt gentle hands on her face. She remembered what her father had once told her. He had said that a visitor from the Spirit World comes to watch over a sick person. "The voice must be here to take me to the Spirit World," Shell-Flower thought.

The voice said, *"Poor little girl, it is too bad."*

Shell-Flower did not know the meaning, but the sound was comforting. She heard it again and again. *"Poor little girl, it is too bad."* Each time, she felt something touching her face.

At last, Shell-Flower began to feel better. She was able to open her eyes. "Someone from the Spirit World sang to me," Shell-Flower said to her mother and grandfather. She told them about the soft voice and the strange words.

"That voice was not from the Spirit World," said Grandfather. "It was the voice of a good white woman who came to care for you. She put some medicine on your face and spoke kind words to you."

Then Shell-Flower heard the voice again. But this time, the words were different.

"You gave your family quite a scare," said the voice. "That poison oak nearly killed you."

Shell-Flower turned to see the smile of the woman who had cared for her. The woman bent down and placed a gentle hand on Shell-Flower's face.

Shell-Flower stared up at the woman's face without speaking. It was not the face of an owl. It seemed kind and beautiful. It was like the face of a sister.

It was the face of a friend.

Several years later, Shell-Flower went to live among white people. She learned to speak, read, and write English. She took an English name: Sarah Winnemucca.

Sarah learned about the ways of white people. She understood that some white people were kind and could be trusted, just as Grandfather had taught. Others were cruel and could not be trusted.

The Northern Paiute suffered as white settlements grew. Sarah Winnemucca tried to do what was best for her people. She spent her life speaking out for fairness, truth, and peace for the Paiute.